The Secret of the Unknown Ghost

Earl Thomas

High Noon Books
Novato, California

Cover Design: Michael Cincotta
Interior Illustrations: Herb Heidinger

Special thanks to Bobby Stinnett and her reading classes at Christiansburg, VA, Middle School for much help with these books.

International Standard Book Number: 0-87879-531-6

9 8 7 6 5 4
4 3 2 1 0 9 8 7 6 5

Contents

CHAPTER 1

Spooky Stories

It was 12:00 noon at the Watson Furniture Factory. Carlos Mendez put down his tools and got his lunch bag. It was time for him to think. Each day at lunch Carlos thought about some new topic or puzzle. Today he was thinking about ghosts.

His friend, P.J. Turner, walked up and sat next to him at the table.

"What are you thinking about today?" P.J. asked.

"Ghosts," Carlos said.

P.J. smiled and said, "Ghosts? Come on, Carlos, you know there is no such thing."

Carlos said, "How do you know?"

P.J. bit into his sandwich. "O.K. then, what

do *you* know about ghosts?"

"Not much but I sure want to know more," Carlos replied.

"Why are you so interested in ghosts today? You didn't talk about ghosts yesterday," P.J. said.

Carlos said, "I wasn't interested in ghosts yesterday. But I am today. I'd like to talk to a real ghost."

"How can you find out if they are real?" P.J. wanted to know.

Carlos bit into an apple. He said, "I've heard that there is a house with a ghost somewhere in Major City."

"A real ghost?" P.J. asked.

"I don't know but I bet we could find out," Carlos said.

"Well, maybe," P.J. said.

Lunch period was over. The whistle sounded. It was time to get back to work.

Carlos had never been in a haunted house.

Most of the ghosts he had read about were in small towns or large, spooky houses in the country. Carlos thought surely there were ghosts in cities, too.

He asked everyone he knew, "Have you ever heard of a ghost in Major City?"

No one he spoke to had ever heard of a ghost in their city.

Then he went to the city library and checked out a book on ghosts. He read stories about old ghosts and new ghosts. He read about ghosts in old country houses and in small towns. But he did not find any stories about ghosts in large cities.

Carlos was sure there must be ghosts in large city houses but where were they?

P.J. told Carlos, "Read a book about how Major City grew. It might tell if there are any ghosts here."

Carlos went back to the city library. He found a copy of a book called *The Story of*

Major City. He checked it out and took it home. He read almost half of the book that first night.

The next night after work he read more.

The last chapter of the book was called "Strange Things of the Past." It had many spooky stories in it but the thing from the past that Carlos liked most was a list of ghost houses. There really were houses in Major City that someone had believed had ghosts. The street addresses of five ghost houses were given.

Carlos thought happily, "Wow! I just knew there were city ghosts somewhere!"

CHAPTER 2

Any Ghosts Today?

Late the next day Carlos and P.J. drove in P.J.'s car to several of the places given in the library book. One place turned out to be right in the middle of the city park.

"Would you believe that once there were houses standing where the softball field is now?" Carlos asked.

"I could believe that as much as I could believe in ghosts," P.J. said. "Come on, let's check the next house on the list."

The next address was on the corner of two very busy streets. The building on the corner did not look as if it would have a ghost in it. In fact, it was a new building with lots of offices.

Carlos and P.J. walked through the

building. They went in one office and talked to the man in charge.

"Do you remember the house that stood here before this building was built?" Carlos asked.

The man said, "Yes. It was an old house. Nobody had lived in it for years."

"Was it a haunted house?" P.J. asked.

The man thought a moment. "Now that you mention it, I think it was. I believe one time someone said they had seen a ghost. After that the house was never rented again."

"I wonder where the ghost went when the house was torn down," Carlos said.

"Don't ask me. There's no ghost here now," the man replied.

Carlos and P.J. drove to the next place. It was getting dark. An old building sat on a lot full of weeds. A large sign on the front door said:

DANGER! STAY AWAY!

P.J. said with a smile, "Hey, that ghost knows how to keep people away."

Carlos stepped back and took a long look at the building. "You're not kidding. Nobody would go into that house because it might cave in."

"Do you want to go in now?" P.J. asked.

"No," Carlos replied.

"Why not?" Have you decided you are afraid of ghosts after all?" P.J. asked.

Carlos started back to the car. "Not until I see one! But I want to wait until we have a flashlight. It would be very dark in there now."

"You're right, Carlos. We'll come back on Saturday," P.J. said.

CHAPTER 3

1201 West Main Street

On Saturday morning P.J. and Carlos walked to the old house. Each of them carried a flashlight.

As they walked, P.J. said, "Maybe we don't need a light today."

Carlos said, "Of course, we need lights. The house has boards over most of the windows."

"My dad says we're crazy to try to find a ghost. He says we have enough problems without trying to find more," P.J. said.

"Why does he think ghosts will be a problem?" Carlos wanted to know.

P.J. said, "I guess he thinks there may be nice ghosts or there may be awful ghosts. No matter which, I know I'd be afraid of a ghost."

Carlos grinned. "We'd both most likely run away the first time we saw a ghost. The second time we could stay for a chat."

They were now standing in front of the house at 1201 West Main Street.

P.J. said, "Somebody owns this house. We should ask to visit before we go in."

"You're right. Let's ask the neighbors. Maybe one of them owns it," Carlos said.

They walked to the nearest house. It did not look very well kept either, but somebody lived there.

They walked up to the front door. P.J. knocked. Nothing happened. After a short wait he knocked again.

Carlos said, "I guess nobody's home."

Just then they heard a noise. A man opened the door. He was much older than Carlos or P.J.

"Well, what do you two want?" he asked.

"Good morning. I am P.J. Turner and this is

my friend Carlos Mendez. Do you own the house next door?" P.J. asked. He pointed to the house.

The man laughed. "That old wreck! Do I look crazy enough to own a place like that?"

"Well, what do you two want?"

"Do you know who owns it?" Carlos asked.

"No, I don't. Nobody's lived there for years," he said.

Carlos asked, "Did you ever see or hear any ghosts over there?"

The man shook his head. "So you're looking for ghosts, huh? Any ghost with an ounce of self-respect wouldn't live in that old place."

"Do you think anybody would care if we went inside and looked?" P.J. asked.

The man said, "Nobody cares." He closed his door.

They walked back to the old house. The front door was locked. They walked around to the side and found a broken window.

They were able to get inside by reaching up, grabbing the window frame, and pulling themselves in.

The first room they went in was empty. No chairs, no tables, small bits of glass from the broken window lay on the floor.

Carlos turned on his flashlight. They walked into another room. It was empty, too. Two doors were in that room. One went into what had been a kitchen. The other door was closed.

P.J. shined his light around. He said, "Where does that door go?"

Carlos opened it. "Great! This is the place!"

P.J. was puzzled. "The place for what, Carlos?"

Carlos said loudly, "The stairs. In stories that's always where people see ghosts!"

P.J. smiled and asked, "Why do they see ghosts on stairs? Do most ghosts live on stairways?"

"I don't know," Carlos said.

"Forget the stairs. I want to go into the basement," P.J. said. He walked in front of Carlos, down the steps, and into a basement.

"No ghosts here," said P.J. He shined the light in all directions.

Carlos had followed him. He looked around. A broken chair sat on one side. A few brown leaves were on the floor. Everything seemed covered with dust.

"I don't see anything ghostly," P.J. said.

"You don't understand, P.J.," Carlos said. "You never see a ghost the first time. We'll have to come back often before we see one."

"You can come here for years if you want to but not me," P.J. said. "Come on, let's go home."

"O.K. I guess that's enough for today," Carlos said.

They left the old house and headed home.

The next Monday at work Carlos and P.J. set a time to go back to the house.

"So you want to go back at midnight on Friday the 13th? Why then?" P.J. wanted to know.

"Midnight is always a good time for ghosts. And Friday the 13th might be a special time," Carlos said.

P.J. said slowly, "Carlos, I don't want to be in a ghost house at midnight."

"O.K. We'll go early. Is nine o'clock a good time for you?" Carlos asked.

"Much better than midnight. We'll go Friday night at nine," P.J. said.

Just then the whistle blew. It was time to get back to work.

Friday night was a quiet and windless night. Carlos and P.J. went into the old house at exactly nine o'clock. They entered through the same window.

They turned on their flashlights and walked quietly through the first two rooms.

"Well, let's find out if ghosts are up and around now," Carlos said as he walked down the steps into the basement. He reached into a trash can and found three dirty metal cans.

"These old tin cans will help us find out if there are any ghosts here," Carlos said.

"How will tin cans tell us anything about ghosts?" P.J. asked.

"I'm not sure, P.J.," Carlos said. "Maybe a lot of noise will stir up some active ghosts."

P.J. said, "Carlos, that's crazy! This is on a busy street. There's a lot of noise around here all day."

"Yes, but that noise is outside, not inside," Carlos replied.

"O.K., give your idea a try and let's see what happens," P.J. said.

Carlos banged two cans together. He did this over and over again.

"That's not enough noise to wake up a beetle," P.J.said with a grin.

"Stand back," Carlos said. He took the cans and threw them one by one against the wall. They made some noise but not a lot.

P.J. shook his head

"Do you have any coins in your pocket?" Carlos asked.

P.J. laughed, "What are you going to do? Pay the ghosts to appear?" He handed a few coins to Carlos.

He took the cans one by one and threw each one against the wall.

Carlos took P.J.'s coins and some from his own pockets. He placed them in a can and began to shake it very fast. The noise was sharp but not very loud.

The house stayed quiet.

Carlos called loudly, "Mr. Ghost, did we wake you?"

P.J. said softly, "Shut up, Carlos. Be quiet and listen."

Both Carlos and P.J. stood for a long time in the same spot. They breathed softly, almost without a sound.

Then they heard a soft noise. A sound was coming from upstairs. It was like a soft note of music.

Carlos and P.J. were frozen. They could not speak. After a few minutes the soft sound stopped.

Carlos said, "Let's get out of here."

P.J. replied, "I'm ready!"

They moved across the basement, up the

stairs, and out the window. Once outside they stopped and looked back at the house. It was very dark. It was very quiet.

Then a small light, almost like a candle, moved in a window for a few seconds and disappeared.

Carlos and P.J. stared at one another. Then they turned and quickly walked away.

CHAPTER 4

Noises in the Night

The next week Carlos and P.J. talked a lot about the ghost house during lunch and while going to and from work.

Wednesday at lunch Carlos said, "I have a new idea about what we can do to find a ghost."

P.J. asked, "Now what's up?"

"Next time we'll wear white sheets," Carlos said.

"Sheets? Why?" P.J. asked.

"Well, we have to do something to get the ghost's attention," Carlos said.

"Why not admit that there are no ghosts? We can't get a ghost's attention if there isn't any such thing," P.J. said.

Carlos frowned. "You may be right. But

we've got to keep on trying."

They talked some more. Finally they decided to go back to the house at midnight on Friday. They would wear sheets.

"We are going to look very silly," P.J. said.

"You may be right," said Carlos with a smile.

Just before midnight on Friday Carlos and P.J. climbed through the broken window once again. Inside they each put on a white sheet.

"I hope the ghost doesn't laugh himself to death," P.J. said.

They walked softly through the house and down the steps into the basement. No sound was heard.

At last Carlos said, "There's no ghost here." He took his sheet off and folded it. P.J. did the same. They walked toward the stairs.

Suddenly they heard a soft sound. It was like a laugh. Over and over again.

Carlos said, "A ghost is laughing at us."

"Carlos, there are no ghosts. Somebody is trying to scare us," P.J. said.

Carlos looked afraid. He tried to talk but no words came out. Finally he was able to say, "What's that laughing?"

P.J. said quickly, "I don't know and I don't care. Let's get out of here."

He rushed up the stairs and to the window. He climbed out. Carlos was close behind.

The next night they were back in the house near midnight. But this time they did not wear sheets.

"What will we do this time? Any ideas?" P.J. wanted to know.

Carlos said, "We've got to do something so the ghost will know we're not crazy."

P.J. grinned. "If there's a ghost in this place, it already knows we're crazy!"

Carlos began walking through all the rooms again. He looked carefully into the corners and behind all the doors. He looked into a small closet in a bedroom.

P.J. followed him. "Carlos, now what are you doing?"

Carlos said, "I am looking for clues."

"Clues to what? Has there been a crime?"

He looked into a small closet in a bedroom.

P.J. asked.

"No crime. I'm looking for a clue to a ghost," Carlos said. He kept looking along the walls and floors.

P.J. said, "How crazy can you be? Ghosts don't leave clues. They don't leave fingerprints or footprints."

Carlos said with a smile. "You never know, P.J."

"Think about those books on ghosts. How did people know that ghosts were there?" P.J. asked.

Carlos said, "They saw the ghosts. Sometimes they heard strange sounds."

"But no clues?" P.J. asked.

"No, no clues," Carlos replied.

P.J. said, "Of course not. Ghosts are not firm and heavy like we are. They can walk through walls without opening them. How can you find clues from things like that?"

"I don't know." Carlos sounded unhappy.

"Carlos, let's sit down and do nothing. Just look and listen," P.J. said.

"O.K. We've tried everything else."

They sat for an hour. They did not talk or whisper. They did not see or hear anything strange.

Finally Carlos said, "P.J., there's no ghost here. Let's go home."

"That's fine with me," P.J. said.

As they walked to the broken window to leave, a sound came from the basement. It was a clicking sound. Click, click. Over and over. It sounded like leather heels clicking against a hard floor.

"Is that the heater making a noise?" Carlos said.

P.J. whispered, "This house has no heater that works."

"Well, something is making a noise in here," Carlos said.

P.J. said softly, "Let's go back to the

basement."

The sounds seemed to come from the center of the basement. Yet nothing was there. No pipes to click together. No heater vents. Then the noise stopped.

After a short wait Carlos yelled, "Ghost, where are you? We want to talk with you."

"You've done it again. If you yell at a ghost, it's not going to yell back," P.J. said.

Carlos said quickly, "Let's come back tomorrow night."

CHAPTER 5

At Last – The Unreal Thing!

The next night Carlos and P.J. climbed into the house at midnight.Somewhere they could hear a clock striking twelve.

"I hope the ghost will make more sounds tonight," Carlos said.

"The sounds we've heard are strange, but is a ghost really making them?" P.J. asked.

"I really don't know," Carlos said.

They walked down the stairs into the basement and sat on the floor in a corner. They could see the stairs clearly.

As they watched, a white form appeared on the steps. It was almost like a thin fog. It seemed to float down the steps and across the basement.

Carlos and P.J. stared. They did not move. The form moved closer. It stopped a few feet from them.

Now it became clearer. Carlos and P.J. could almost see a man's face and hands. No legs, no feet, and at first no sound.

Carlos and P.J. were frozen. Then they heard a very soft voice. The sound was a whisper.

The voice said. "You . . . want . . . to . . . talk." There was a brief pause after each word.

Carlos could not speak. He moved his lips but no words came out.

The voice said again, "You . . . want . . . to . . . talk."

P.J. found his voice. "Are you a real ghost?"

"What . . . do . . . you . . . think?" the voice asked.

"I think you must be a ghost!" P.J. said.

The form vanished!

Carlos and P.J. looked from side to side and up and down. The form was gone.

P.J. pushed hard on Carlos' arm. "Snap out of it, Carlos."

Carlos blinked his eyes a few times. Then he said, "Hey! Wow! That was a ghost. That was a ghost!"

P.J. said, "You are the one who has said for weeks you wanted to talk to a ghost. But you didn't say a word!"

Carlos nodded. "I was scared. You were great, P.J."

"Next time we see a ghost you are going to do the talking," P.J. said.

"I will! I will! I'll talk next time we see the ghost. I hope it will be real soon," Carlos said.

"Let's go home," P.J. said.

"Yes, let's go but we've got to come back very soon," Carlos said.

As they walked home, Carlos said, "P.J., I'm going back to that basement every night."

P.J. yawned. "Carlos, you can go back to the house whenever you want to. Not me. I can't talk with ghosts at night and stay awake to work the next day."

Each day the next week they talked about the ghost. Each night Carlos went to the house. But he did not see the ghost. And each day at work he yawned a lot.

He kept telling P.J. at lunch, "I'm sure I will see our ghost friend tonight."

"I hope you do," P.J. told him. "I'll go with you on Friday night. Good luck."

Carlos yawned again.

On Friday Carlos and P.J. were inside the old house before midnight. They sat in the basement and talked softly.

Near midnight Carlos said, "Each night I have called loudly to the ghost. But I didn't get any answer."

P.J. asked, "Why did you call out? Did you ever think that the ghost might prefer a softer greeting?"

"I thought I needed to make a lot of noise to let him know I was here," Carlos said.

P.J. said, "Well, tonight let's be very quiet. We won't talk at all."

"O.K.," Carlos said.

They sat on the floor of the basement and made no sound. They even tried to breathe quietly. The minutes seemed to pass very slowly.

"I don't think he is here tonight," Carlos said in a whisper.

P.J. was looking toward the stairs. "Oh, yes he is. I can see him."

Carlos turned. They both watched a ghost form float down the steps. It just stood there not making a sound.

Slowly Carlos and P.J. stood up. They walked a few steps toward the form. It looked like fog or smoke in the shape of a man. As they moved closer, the ghost became a little easier to see. They stopped and waited.

They could not see a clear face. They could see the soft shape of a head and a body. The form seemed to be standing with no part of it touching the floor. It seemed to float when it moved.

"Who are you?" Carlos asked loudly.

The ghost did not answer.

"We are glad to see you," P.J. said softly.

A sound came from the ghost. It was hard to hear. Only by listening carefully could they hear it say, "Oh, thank . . . you . . . for . . . speaking . . . softly."

"We are happy to see you," P.J. whispered.

Then the ghost said, "People . . . are . . . afraid . . . of . . . me . . . Why?"

P.J. said, "I think it is because you are different."

Then Carlos said, "You can appear and disappear without walking in or out. That scares people."

The ghost seemed to turn to Carlos. The move was quick. Carlos stepped back. He looked afraid.

The ghost said in its soft voice, "I . . . don't . . . like . . . you. You . . . make . . . too . . . much . . . noise."

Carlos said in a soft voice. "I'm very sorry. I did not know."

The ghost seemed to tremble a little. It said, "You . . . yell . . . You . . . shout . . . without . . . thinking."

"I will be careful to talk softly from now on," Carlos whispered.

"Thank . . . you," said the ghost.

P.J. asked, "We would be very pleased if you would talk with us some more. We promise not to yell."

The ghost said, "I . . . have . . . a . . . story . . . to . . . tell. But . . . not . . . tonight."

The ghost stopped talking, floated toward the stairs, and disappeared.

"Thank you," Carlos said loudly.

"Carlos," P.J. said. "You forgot again. Lower your voice. Let's get out of here before he changes his mind."

They left quickly. It had been a night to remember!

CHAPTER 6

The Ghost's Story

The next day Carlos and P.J. went to the Records Office of Major City.

"We need to find out who owns the house," Carlos said.

"Why?" asked P.J.

"So we can find out if the person will make some repairs. That house needs work," Carlos said.

"Oh, Carlos, that ghost doesn't care if the roof leaks or if it's cold in winter," P.J. said.

"That's true. But he wouldn't like it if the house were torn down. And if repairs aren't made, that's what will happen," Carlos said.

P.J. said, "Why do you think he is in this house? What's going on?"

"I don't know. But he's there for a good reason. I'm sure of that," Carlos said.

At the Records Office they asked about the owner of the house at 1201 West Main Street.

Carlos asked the clerk, "Do you think there will be time to find the owner's name today?"

The clerk smiled. We will know in two minutes or less. Our records are on computer tapes. I can push a few keys and the computer will tell us the owner's name."

"Wow!" said Carlos.

The clerk sat in front of the computer. She pushed a few keys and waited. P.J. and Carlos watched.

Then the clerk stood up and wrote a few words on a piece of paper.

She handed the paper to them."Here is the owner's name and address."

Carlos and P.J. read the words on the paper: "Owner – Mrs. Sue Nash. Address – West Side Apartments, No. 16."

Carlos said, "Let's go see her now."

P.J. turned back to the clerk and said, "Thank you very much! You have been a great help."

Carlos and P.J. dashed out of the office and drove to the West Side Apartments.

They talked with Sue Nash, the owner of the old house. She was helpful.

Carlos asked, "Do you plan on repairing the house?"

Mrs. Nash said, "I'd like to put on a new roof and make some other repairs. But it would cost a lot of money."

P.J. asked a lot of questions. Finally he asked, "Mrs. Nash, did you know that there's a ghost in your house?"

"Many years ago the person who lived there said there was a ghost but I didn't believe it," Mrs. Nash replied.

Carlos said loudly, "Well, you better believe it now because a ghost is really there.

Would you like to see it?"

Mrs. Nash was quiet. Then she said, "Yes, I'd like to see a ghost who lives in my house."

That night Carlos and P.J. took Mrs. Nash with them when they went to the old house. It

"Yes, I would like to see the ghost who lives in my house."

was close to midnight when the three of them walked across the front lawn.

As they walked to the window, the man from next door walked up and spoke to them. It was the man Carlos and P.J. had talked to a few days earlier.

He said, "Hey! I'm Jim Smith. You two guys came by my house a few days ago. I told you I didn't want to talk about ghosts. I've changed my mind. I want to go in the house with you."

"Mrs. Nash, the owner of the house, is with us tonight," Carlos said.

"We are not sure the ghost will appear if too many people are there," P.J. said.

Mr. Smith said loudly, "Who does this house belong to – Mrs. Nash or the ghost?"

"Mrs. Nash," Carlos said.

"Then you let her tell me if I can go inside," Mr. Smith said.

Mrs. Nash said softly, "Mr. Smith, we want

to talk to the ghost if we can."

Mr. Smith looked angry. "You people want to go into a dark house at midnight and talk with a ghost! You must be crazy!"

"Then you shouldn't go in with us. We crazy people might get you into trouble," Mrs. Nash answered with a smile.

Mr. Smith said, "O.K., I won't go in with you. But you better do some repair work on this old house or the city will make you tear it down."

Mrs. Nash said, "I'll think about it."

Carlos, P.J., and Mrs. Nash walked to the window and began climbing in. Mr. Smith watched as they did. Then he turned and walked away.

Inside the house they walked to the top of the stairs. Flashlights showed them the way down the stairs into the basement.

It was a very short wait for the ghost. They had barely settled themselves in a sitting position when they saw him floating down the steps.

The ghost did the same thing he had done before. He moved slowly across the basement to the middle. He paused there.

P.J. and Carlos got up and walked toward him. Mrs. Nash got up but she stayed behind Carlos and P.J.

P.J. said, "Hello. We are glad to see you."

The form became clearer and easier to see. It said, "Hello . . ." It seemed to be looking toward Mrs. Nash.

Carlos said, "This lady is the owner of this house."

P.J. said, "We didn't know who the owner was until today."

"We told her that you were here. She wanted to come to see you," Carlos said.

The form turned toward Carlos. It said, "I . . . hope. . . you . . . keep . . . your . . . voice . . . soft."

Then the ghost looked at Mrs. Nash.

P.J. said softly, "We want to hear your story. You told us that you would tell it to us tonight."

The ghost turned to P.J. and said in a tone so low it was hard to hear, "Yes . . . I . . ."

Carlos, P.J., and Mrs. Nash sat on the floor. The ghost remained standing.

The face of the ghost was clearer, almost clear enough to be a person. He did not speak for a few seconds. He seemed to be getting ready for the story.

P.J. turned around and saw that Mrs. Nash was watching the ghost very closely. He had thought she might be afraid of the ghost but she didn't seem to be.

The ghost began to talk. "At . . . one . . . time . . . I . . . lived . . . near . . . here . . . My . . . name . . . was . . . Bill."

The ghost stopped talking for a few seconds. Then he began again. "I . . . was . . . in

. . . love . . . with . . . a . . . girl . . . We . . . talked . . . about . . . getting . . . married . . . I . . . gave . . . her . . . a . . . ring . . . Then . . . the . . . army . . . sent . . . me . . . to . . . fight . . ."

The ghost stopped. Carlos and P.J. expected

"Was your name Bill King?"

him to leave. Then they heard loud sobs behind them.

Mrs. Nash stood up. She said to the ghost, "Was your name Bill King?"

The ghost spoke again, "Was . . . your . . . name . . . Sue Stone?"

She said, "Yes! Yes! I was very much in love with Bill King. He was killed in the war. I almost died from grief. I never believed I'd see you again, Bill."

The ghost was silent for a long time. Then it said, "Are . . . you . . . happy . . . Sue?"

"Oh, yes," Sue Nash said.

"Tell . . . me . . . about . . . yourself . . . ," the ghost said.

"Well, I'm married with a daughter and a son." She stopped, then said, "I named my son Bill."

This time the ghost spoke with no pauses. "If you are happy, I no longer need to return. I can rest in peace."

Sue had tears in her eyes. "That is what I want for you – peace."

Carlos said loudly, "Now we don't ever have to be afraid of ghosts again."

"Shhush," said the ghost and promptly disappeared.